ELM PUBLICATIONS
WRITTEN AND ILLUSTRATED BY EMMET MC NAMARA
ISBN 9781999683184
PRINTED BY PRECISION PRINT
GRAPHIC DESIGN BY JAY KENNA

Rory, the bus Man prepares for work.

He is in a good mood.

Rory stands beside his green bus.

He is looking forward to talking
to the passengers.

He is in his cab;
it is like a second home for him.

Rory climbs into the seat and begins work.

The bus tumbles along the road.

Rory is always careful when driving the bus.

Jim, the runner, chases the bus,
Rory will stop for him.

Rory enjoys his job.

**The Bus climbs Kilmore hill,
everybody likes the view.**

The Town is at the bottom of the hill.

Mary and Jane wait for the bus.

They look forward to seeing Rory
and his green bus.

Rory stops the bus
and greets Mary and Jane.

"Hello, how are you" Rory says.

Rory stops the bus and has lunch.

He has a ham roll and a bottle of pop.

Rory drives the bus through a rain storm.

He is warm in his cab.

Work time ends for the Day.

Rory parks the bus in the Depot.